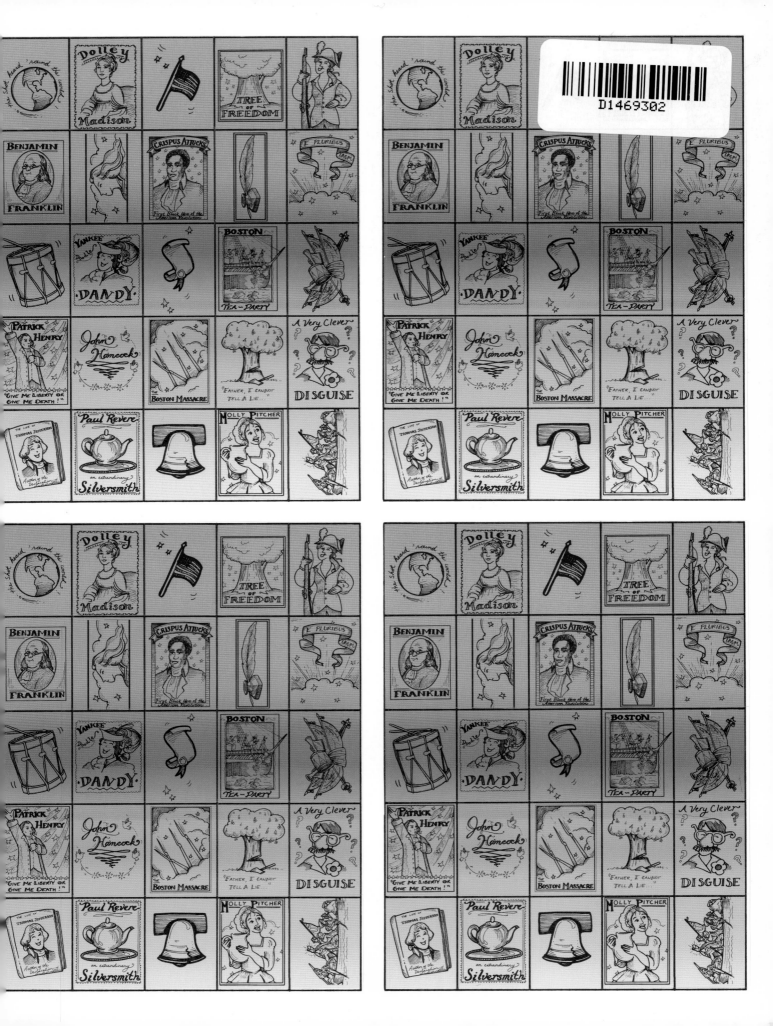

United States History
The American Revolution

By
Jane Pofahl

Cover Illustration and Inside Illustrations By
Darcy Myers

Publishers
T.S. Denison & Company, Inc.
Minneapolis, Minnesota 55431

Standard Book Number: 513-02223-6
United States History—The American Revolution
Copyright © 1994 by T.S. Denison & Co., Inc.
9601 Newton Avenue South
Minneapolis, Minnesota 55431

Introduction

History is the living record of the human race—exciting as it is varied. *The Time Traveler Series* will aid you as you teach the colorful history of America to your children and explore such topics as the early explorers, settlement of the colonies, the American Revolution, westward movement, and historic personalities who helped shape our own present-day culture.

After each topic is presented, activity pages are provided for your children to implement suggested vocabulary, conduct further research, and provide creative answers/solutions to historical situations. Fun reproducible pages are also included to review the historical and cultural facts studied on the preceding pages.

Each book contains the following:

- topic information pages
- research/activity pages (including maps, charts, research topics, and creative thinking activities)
- reproducible activity pages
- time period stickers

The Time Traveler Series was created to spark the intrigue of your children and lay a foundation for enjoyable history instruction and learning. Have fun!

Table of Contents

The Boston Massacre

In 1768, King George III of England was not amused. The colonists in America were smuggling goods into the country to avoid paying taxes on English products such as lead, glass, paint, paper, wine, and tea. King George decided to show the colonists who was in control, and he sent 4,000 British troops under the command of General Thomas Gage to Boston, as well as a flotilla of warships, to uphold law and order.

Now the Bostonians were not amused. They resented the presence of the British Redcoats, or "Lobsterbacks," in their city. The British soldiers caused trouble in the streets and taverns. Soldiers could search the colonists' homes at any time, and the colonists could not keep weapons in their homes to defend themselves. If the colonists were approached, they had to give the soldiers food and lodging, or quartering, in their own homes. On top of these indignities, the colonists were being taxed heavily by the British government without their consent. Cries of "Taxation without representation!" were heard throughout the colonies.

Early in 1770, tension mounted in Boston. Hundreds of British soldiers were shipped back to England in an attempt to pacify angry Bostonians. It did not work.

On March 5, 1770, a group of schoolboys taunted a British guard in front of the Customs House. Soon the boys were joined by others who hurled snowballs as well as insults at the guard. After the guard called for help, a squad of Redcoats ran down the street to put down the riot that was starting.

A British musket went off, and then more shots were fired into the angry crowd and over their heads. When the fighting was over, five colonists were dead and many more were wounded. One of the Bostonians was Crispus Attucks, the first black hero of the American Revolution.

Eight British soldiers and their commander, Captain Thomas Preston, were taken into custody and charged with murder. Patriot leader Samuel Adams called the incident a "massacre," and used it to create anti-British sentiments throughout the colonies. His lawyer cousin, John Adams, was asked to defend the British soldiers. Wanting to prove to the world the American belief that "all men are innocent until proven guilty" and that Americans were a just people, John Adams took the case. Captain Preston was acquitted, six soldiers were found not guilty, and two were found guilty of manslaughter. They were each burned on the thumb with a hot branding iron and released.

The Boston Massacre

RESEARCH QUESTIONS

1. In a dictionary, find the following words: *massacre, smuggling, flotilla, tavern, indignity, consent, representation, pacify, taunt, musket, custody, incident, sentiment, acquitted,* and *manslaughter.* Define each and use it in a sentence.

2. John Adams will go on to play an even greater part in American history. Find out more about John Adams and present your findings in a report.

3. Samuel Adams used *propaganda* to make a street fight into a massacre. Make a chart of six examples of propaganda used in advertising to influence people.

PROJECTS

1. People throughout the colonies learned about the Boston Massacre from posters illustrated by Samuel Adams' friend, Paul Revere. Make a poster to tell what really happened in Boston on March 5, 1770.

2. To see the struggle with the colonies in Boston before the Revolution from the British point of view, read *Redcoat in Boston,* by Ann Finlayson.

3. Samuel Adams declared March 5th to be a "Day of Mourning" in Boston. Why do you think he wants people to remember such a sad event every year?

The Boston Tea Party

Colonists loved to drink tea. They were used to drinking it in England, and when they settled in the New World, they continued the custom of drinking tea much the same as people drink a cup of coffee today.

The British knew of the colonists' fondness for tea, and placed a sales tax on it in the colonies. Americans rebelled at the cost, and either grew their own tea or started smuggling tea from the Netherlands. In 1773, the British Parliament passed the Tea Act in which tea sold to the colonies was lower in price than either the Netherlands brand or the kind grown in the colonies. The British believed that the colonists would buy the less expensive British tea and forget about all the anger over "taxation without representation."

Patriot Samuel Adams in Boston did not want to forget about it. He did not want others to forget, either. On the night of December 16, 1773, hundreds of American citizens from Boston and the surrounding area came together at Old South Church in Boston to discuss what should be done about the latest load of tea brought into Boston Harbor by the cargo ship, the Dartmouth. If Britain's official, Governor Hutchinson, agreed to sending the tea back to England, no action would be taken by the colonists. However, the governor refused to sign the order to return the tea. Samuel Adams said the code words, "This meeting can do nothing more to save the country," and the Boston Tea Party began.

Fifty men with faces smeared with soot and paint to look like Mohawk Indians marched in twos to the harbor. As they reached the dock, the men divided into three groups. Once they boarded the Dartmouth, the Beaver, and the Eleanor, their duties were the same. The first mate was located and asked for the keys to the hold. He was assured that if the crew did not resist, there would be no trouble. The Mohawks systematically removed all of the casks and chests containing tea and threw them into Boston Harbor. The water was so shallow in places and the amount of tea was so great that some of the loose tea spilled back onto one of the ships. The men participating in the Tea Party were sworn to secrecy, and agreed not to take any of the tea so that it would be an act of protest, not theft. They also agreed to clean up the ship and leave it exactly as they had found it—minus the tea. Mohawks, as well as sympathetic sailors, swept the decks clean. A lock broken by mistake was noted and replaced the next day. The Mohawks filed off the ship in an orderly manner, and to the tune of "Yankee Doodle Dandy," marched by twos through the street of Boston to their homes.

The Boston Tea Party

RESEARCH QUESTIONS

1. In a dictionary, find the following words: *rebel* (verb), *smuggling*, *official*, *soot*, *systematic*, *cask*, *shallow*, *secrecy*, and *sympathetic*. Define each word and use it in a sentence.

2. *Samuel Adams* made a habit of stirring up people. Find out more about the life of Samuel Adams, then dress up like him and tell the group the story of his life from his point of view.

3. One of the "Mohawks" involved in the Boston Tea Party was really *Paul Revere*. Find out more about Paul Revere and draw examples of his works as a silversmith.

PROJECTS

1. If you had lived in Boston on December 16, 1773, would you have taken part in the Boston Tea Party? Why or why not?

2. The novel, *Johnny Tremain* by Ester Forbes, tells the adventures of an apprentice to Paul Revere during the exciting events of the prerevolutionary Boston. After you read the book, watch the Disney video.

3. In two years, Paul Revere will make his famous ride to warn John Adams and John Hancock that the British are coming to Concord. Read the poem "Paul Revere's Ride" by Longfellow. Then read *Jack Juett's Ride* by Gail Haley and compare the two rides.

The Declaration of Independence

The First Continental Congress was called in September, 1774. The delegates agreed that the states would boycott British goods in an effort to force Britain to end taxation without representation. The delegates also agreed to meet in a year's time if Britain did not change its policies. Britain did not.

The Second Continental Congress met in Philadelphia, Pennsylvania, on May 10, 1775. John Hancock was the Chairman for the Congress. Delegates voted to organize an army and a navy. They sent a final appeal to King George III, asking for the repeal, or end, of the unfair taxes. King George never replied.

Early in 1776, Thomas Paine wrote his popular pamphlet entitled *Common Sense*. It stated that it was only "common sense" to break away from Britain and become an independent nation. Many colonists agreed with him.

On June 7, 1776, Congress agreed that the colonies were free and independent states, and a committee was formed to write a document stating this fact to Britain. The members of the committee were John Adams, Benjamin Franklin, Robert Livingston, Roger Sherman, and the author of the document, Thomas Jefferson.

The Declaration includes a preamble (or introduction) and three sections. The first section declares the rights of the citizens of the United States, followed by a section stating the wrongs done by Britain against the United States, and ending with a section stating freedom and independence from Britain.

Many famous men in American history signed the Declaration. Among the fifty-six signatures can be found the names of John Adams, Samuel Adams, Benjamin Franklin, Thomas Jefferson, John Hancock, Robert Livingston, and Roger Sherman. It was an act of courage to sign the document, because if the United States lost the war, every man who signed it would be hanged for treason against Britain.

The Declaration of Independence is on display, under glass, in the National Archives Building in Washington, D.C.

The Declaration of Independence

RESEARCH QUESTIONS

1. In a dictionary, find the following words: *continental, congress, delegate, repeal, pamphlet, preamble, treason,* and *archive.* Define each word and use it in a sentence.

2. Draw a map of Pennsylvania. Locate and identify the cities of Philadelphia and Allentown, the Delaware River, and the Susquehanna River.

3. Find out more about the author of the Declaration of Independence, *Thomas Jefferson.* Make a picture book of the significant events in his life.

4. Find out more about Thomas Paine. Was "Common Sense" his only famous writing? Write a resumé, or list, of his life accomplishments.

PROJECTS

1. Watch the musical video, *1776,* about the signing of the Declaration of Independence.

2. Why do you think John Hancock wrote his signature on the Declaration of Independence so large? Practice writing your name in cursive, using lots of curls and flourishes.

3. Not everyone in the colonies wanted independence from Britain. Those who remained loyal to Britain during the Revolution were called *Tories.* Read *The Scarlet Badge,* by Wilma Pitchford Hays, for a look at the Revolution from a Tory point of view.

4. Knowing that Britain has every advantage of winning the war and if America loses you will be hung for treason, would you have signed the Declaration of Independence? Why or why not?

Extra! Extra!

You are a reporter for the Salem Sentinel. You've just heard that the Continental Congress meeting in Independence Hall is voting on a declaration stating the colonies are free from Britain. Wow! This is big new for the folks back home in Massachusetts! While you wait for the official story on the declaration, you draw a picture of Independence Hall in the space below to illustrate your story.

Benjamin Franklin

When Benjamin Franklin was ten years old in 1716, his father removed him from school in his hometown of Boston, Massachusetts, because young Benjamin was poor in mathematics. His father felt that paying for Ben's schooling was a waste of money, and set Benjamin into work in the family's soap and candle shop. Little did Josiah Franklin know that his newest candle maker would become one of the most famous men in American history.

Benjamin only had two years of schooling, but he was a student all of his life. He read the works of great scholars, writers, and scientists. He taught himself algebra, geometry, navigation, grammar, logic, and science. He even learned the basics of French, German, Italian, Spanish, and Latin!

When Benjamin was twelve, he worked in his brother James' print shop. The brothers did not get along well, and at seventeen, Benjamin ran away to the bustling city of Philadelphia in Pennsylvania. Benjamin worked hard for many printers for seven years, and in 1730, he became the owner and publisher of *The Pennsylvania Gazette.* In 1730, he also married Deborah Reed, with whom he would have two sons and a daughter.

As well as publishing *The Pennsylvania Gazette* and *Poor Richard's Almanac,* Benjamin Franklin was an inventor. His inventions included the Franklin stove, bifocal glasses, and the lightning rod. He refused to patent any of his inventions and considered them his way of making life better for everyone.

Benjamin Franklin also helped to improve the colonists' lives by organizing the first postal service. He started the first library in the colonies, the first fire department, the first hospital, and the University of Pennsylvania in order to make Philadelphia a better city.

He is best known for his roles as diplomat and peacemaker during the turbulent early years of the United States. He was a member of the Second Continental Congress and a signer of the Declaration of Independence. Franklin's influence helped persuade the French to join the Americans in fighting the British during the Revolution. He also signed the Treaty of Paris, the Treaty of Peace with Britain, and the Constitution. Benjamin Franklin died on April 17, 1790, at the age of 84.

Benjamin Franklin

RESEARCH QUESTIONS

1. In a dictionary, find the following words: *algebra, grammar, logic, almanac, bifocal, patent, diplomat,* and *turbulent.* Define each word and use it in a sentence.

2. Research the different kinds of printing presses. Find pictures of the kind used by Benjamin Franklin, and tell how it was operated.

3. Did you know that there was a state for four years in the United States called "Franklin," in honor of Benjamin Franklin? Find out about it and report your findings to the group.

4. Benjamin Franklin's picture is on one of our bills of *currency.* On which bill is his picture?

PROJECTS

1. Choose one of Benjamin Franklin's inventions. Make a model of it and explain how it works.

2. Benjamin Franklin's *The Pennsylvania Gazette* was the first newspaper in the colonies to use *cartoons* to make fun of politicians. Find a political cartoon in a newspaper and explain the point the cartoonist is making.

3. Benjamin Franklin wrote *Poor Richard's Almanac,* known for its witty sayings, such as "The early bird catches the worm," and "A penny saved is a penny earned." After reading examples of sayings from *Poor Richard's Almanac,* write your own wise words on anything in your life—homework, school lunch, or even bubblegum!

Benjamin Franklin Crossword

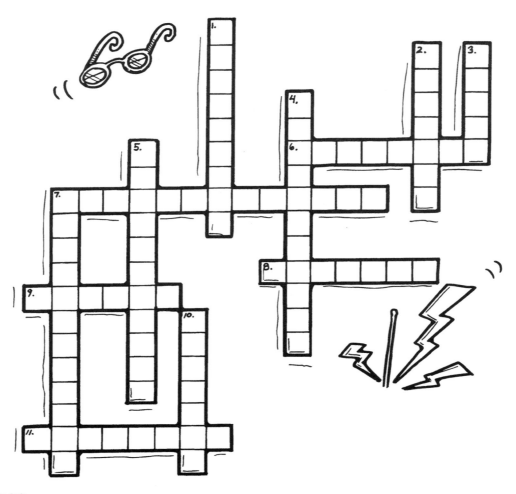

ACROSS:

6. Glasses which have two lenses, one for seeing long distance and one for seeing short distance.
7. The machine Benjamin Franklin used to create *The Pennsylvania Gazette*.
8. The basic parts of speech.
9. Official document saying that you are the creator of a new invention.
11. A person skilled in negotiating with people.

DOWN:

1. In a stormy or agitated state.
2. Place which holds lots of books; Benjamin Franklin organized the first one in the colonies.
3. Benjamin Franklin's older brother.
4. Benjamin Franklin's wife.
5. Inventor of bifocals, the lightning rod, and the Franklin stove.
7. The city Benjamin Franklin loved best.
10. Poor Richard's _ _ _ _ _ _ _ .

Major Revolutionary War Battles

The British and the Americans had different styles of warfare. The British used the traditional European battle formation of marching in ranks wearing brightly colored tailored uniforms, and forming two lines so that when the first line of defense fell, there would be another behind to take its place. The Americans adopted the Indians method of bushfighting, or hiding behind trees and rocks and peppering the enemy with sniper fire. Patriots wore a variety of clothing, but the most consistent piece of attire worn by the Americans was the three-cornered hat.

The first battles of the Revolutionary War were fought at the towns of Lexington and Concord in Massachusetts. On April 19, 1775, more than 2,000 British soldiers set out to destroy American ammunition supplies in Concord. They were stopped at Lexington by colonial Minutemen, and the gunfire known as the "shot heard 'round the world" began the Revolution. The patriots lost eight men in the fighting. A few hours later in Concord, the Redcoats were forced back from North Bridge by hundreds of patriots. The British lost over 300 men, the Americans less than a hundred.

Did you know that the battle of Bunker Hill was really fought on Breed's Hill? The militiamen of Boston wanted to mount cannons atop Breed's Hill and Bunker Hill overlooking the major seaport, but were defeated by British warships and foot soldiers on June 17, 1775. However, it was considered a victory for the patriots because nearly 1,100 British were killed in the fighting.

The battle of Trenton, New Jersey, was fought on December 26, 1776. The British and Hessian (German) soldiers had General George Washington trapped with his 2,400 troops in an inlet of the icy Delaware River. In a daring move, Washington led his freezing troops by night across the Delaware River in small boats on a surprise attack of the sleeping British and Hessians.

The turning point of the Revolutionary War was at Saratoga, New York, in October of 1777. British General "Gentleman" Johnny Burgoyne was defeated by the decisive leadership of General Benedict Arnold. The victory at Saratoga convinced the French that America could win the war, and it joined in the fight against Britain.

The final battle of the Revolution occurred at Yorktown, Virginia, from September 28 to October 19, 1781. British commander Lord Cornwallis stationed his men on the peninsula at Yorktown. Early in September, French battleships defeated the British fleet in Chesapeake Bay. General Washington's and French General Rochambeau's forces trapped Cornwallis on the peninsula with no way to escape by land or water. On October 19, Cornwallis surrendered his army to Washington, and the American Revolution was over.

Major Revolutionary War Battles

RESEARCH QUESTIONS

1. In a dictionary, find the following *words: traditional, sniper, ammunition, militia, decisive,* and *peninsula.* Define each word and use it in a sentence.

2. Find the dates for the following Revolutionary War battles: Trenton, Lexington and Concord, Saratoga, Bunker Hill, Fort Ticonderoga, Yorktown, and Charleston. Make a timeline of major Revolutionary War battles.

3. The French Revolution took place from 1789 to 1799. France helped America during its war—did America help France? Find out more about the French Revolution, and write your findings in the form of a newspaper story.

4. Find a picture of a British soldier in uniform and a militiaman dressed for battle. Draw pictures of both and write a paragraph comparing and contrasting their clothing.

PROJECTS

1. The Revolutionary War was also fought at sea. John Paul Jones uttered the famous words, "I have not yet begun to fight!" while fighting the British in the North Sea. Find out about the *Bonhomme Richard* and make a model of it.

2. An excellent four-book series on the Revolutionary War was written by Leonard Wibberly. Choose from *John Treegate's Musket, Peter Treegate's War, Sea Captain from Salem,* or *Treegate's Raiders.*

3. To find out more about the occupation of Philadelphia by British General Howe, read *Rebecca's War,* by Ann Finlayson.

4. How accurate were muskets? Read about Revolutionary War weapons and compare them with modern day weapons.

5. Choose your favorite land or sea battle from the Revolutionary War. make a diorama depicting the battle.

6. Why was the first gunshot at Lexington called the "shot heard 'round the world?"

Major Revolutionary War Battles

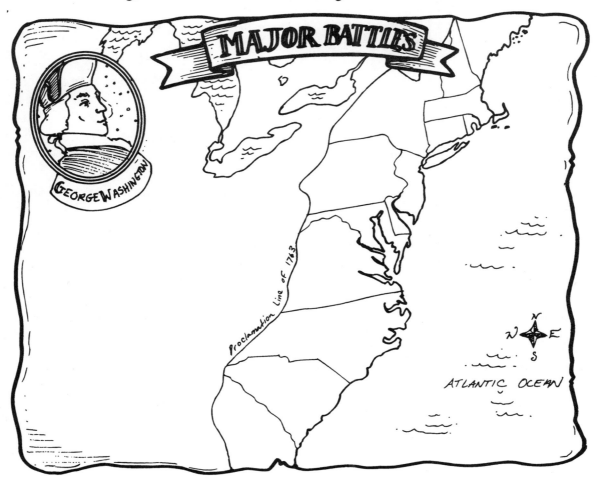

1. Identify the following battle sites on your map (refer to encyclopedia or resource books for help):
   - Lexington
   - Concord
   - Saratoga
   - Valley Forge
   - Trenton
   - Philadelphia
   - Yorktown
   - Ticonderoga, NY
   - Bunker Hill
   - Charleston

2. Name the city in South Carolina which fell to Sir Henry Clinton.

   _____

3. Name the city in Pennsylvania which was occupied by British General Howe. _____

4. Name the place where General Washington kept his troops during the bitter winter of 1777. _____

5. Name the city where Cornwallis surrendered to Washington in 1781.

   _____

Heroic Men in the Revolutionary War

It is a strange fact that extraordinary events bring out the extraordinary in people. War is an extraordinary event, and it brought out the extraordinary in many colonists during the Revolutionary War.

One such man was Crispus Attucks. On March 5, 1770, he became involved in the Boston Massacre, a street fight provoked by the colonists against British soldiers. Attucks and four other Americans were killed. In life he was a freedman sailor in the port of Boston until his ship sailed, but in death he became the first black hero of the Revolution.

Patrick Henry was another man who rose to the challenges presented to him and met them with courage. Born and raised in Virginia, Henry became a lawyer and used his talent for public speaking in 1764 when he was elected to the House of Burgesses. He fought for the rights of the colonists against those who favored British policies. He was a member of the Sons of Liberty, a group opposed to British interference in colonial life. His most famous speech, against the Stamp Act in 1775, ended with the words, "Give me liberty or give me death!" He helped guide the struggling nation by serving in the First and Second Continental Congresses, as governor of Virginia, and by helping to write the first ten amendments to the Constitution, known as the Bill of Rights.

Some men proved their valor in battle. Ethan Allen was a rebel from the frontiers of Vermont and New York. Allen organized his Green Mountain Boys to help Colonel Benedict Arnold capture Fort Ticonderoga, located in upstate New York, from the British in 1775.

A man who was tested to extraordinary limits during the Revolution was George Washington. Having gained military experience during the French and Indian War, Washington was elected unanimously by the Second Continental Congress to become Commander-in-Chief of the American army in 1775. General Washington and his men suffered many hardships, including freezing temperatures, inadequate clothing, poor quality of food, contagious diseases, and shortages of supplies. Desertion of soldiers was another problem. Despite these setbacks, Washington joined with Rochambeau to corner Cornwallis at Yorktown in 1781, ending with the Revolution. Washington went on to become president of the Constitutional convention in 1787, and was elected the first President of the United States, serving from 1789 to 1797.

Heroic Men in the Revolutionary War

RESEARCH QUESTIONS

1. In a dictionary, find the following words: *heroic, extraordinary, provoke, lawyer, interference, amendment, unanimous, contagious,* and *desertion.* Define each word and use it in a sentence.

2. Choose one of the heroic patriots in your reading: *Crispus Attucks, Patrick Henry, Ethan Allen,* or *George Washington.* Find out about his life and accomplishments. Present your findings to the group as if you were *inducting* him into the American Hall of Fame.

3. George Washington's home is located at Mount Vernon, Virginia. Research the history of Mount Vernon. Write a one-page summary and draw a picture of Washington's home.

PROJECTS

1. Read *Where was Patrick Henry on the 29th of May?* by Jean Fritz. If you were Patrick Henry, of what accomplishment would you be most proud? Why?

2. Draw the design for a stamp *commemorating* Crispus Attucks and the Boston Massacre.

3. You are a member of the *Sons of Liberty.* Write you reasons for declaring a new national holiday—Ethan Allen Day.

4. It is a tall tale that George Washington chopped down a cherry tree and did not lie to his father about it. Create another tall tale about George Washington as a boy.

Heroic Men Wordfind

```
C N L S O P T T V C R Y X B Q X H S X Q S
L A W Y E R O G J Y A Y D Q X J X T Q D P
L X O D R O R O A K V P R B E K A T M X C
E N S B S V U K P I K H V V B V G I R W J
N K D F U O P G T N X B D S K F N M D H S
W E H Z W K A C R T S P Y E V C H Q I M D
C Q V H G E O R G E W A S H I N G T O N B
V G O N B X X I P R E T H A N A L L E N V
V U R T M T Z S I F I R Y M Y K N S B E Q
G S S P S R R P Z E Q I H E R O I C X J O
E J G M T A E U N R N C O N T A G I O U S
R O Z N Z O B S Q E K K U D B K B C N Q G
C I K G R R U A H N K H N M W V J O I X A
S V M A O D L T N C D E S E R T I O N Y W
R B J S X I M T E E U N A N I M O U S G T
Q F P A Y N G U O I T R W T R I L I O X T
M G W C J A P C H P H Y T W G P G F U A X
J O A N E R F K X J M Q N K I T P U Y Q O
H W W N R Y L S B A K B E G I G J L R X H
```

Can you find these words?

GEORGE WASHINGTON   CRISPUS ATTUCKS   EXTRAORDINARY
PATRICK HENRY   INTERFERENCE   ETHAN ALLEN
CONTAGIOUS   DESERTION   UNANIMOUS
AMENDMENT   PROVOKE   LAWYER
                     HEROIC

Heroic Women in the Revolutionary War

In the 1700s, a woman's place was in the home. Women were expected to make the food, care for the children, wash the clothes, and run the household. When the war broke out and their fathers, husbands, and brothers left to fight, women had to run businesses, tend cattle, and plow fields as well as care for their families. In addition, women organized food and clothing drives to send items such as salted meats and hand-knitted woolen socks to their men in the battlefields.

Some women chose to serve their country in more untraditional ways. On the night of April 26, 1777, sixteen-year-old Sybil Ludington rode all night long on her horse, Star, to the farms and villages near Ludingtons' Mills, New York. She warned the sleeping Minutemen that the British had burned the city of Danbury and were marching toward them. The men assembled in time and the British retreated, thanks to the courage of Sybil Ludington.

Another brave heroine of the war was Molly Pitcher. Her real name was Mary Ludwig. Following her husband onto the battlefield, she cooked, washed, and sewed for the men. She even brought cool water to them in her pitcher, so the men nicknamed her "Molly Pitcher." After the war, Molly was given a yearly pension of $40 from the government in gratitude for her service.

Margaret Corbin also traveled with her husband during the war. When her husband was killed while firing the cannon at Fort Washington in New York, Margaret replaced him at the cannon and fought until she was seriously injured. She also received a pension from the government and is buried in the military cemetery at West Point, New York.

The most unusual story of a woman in the war belongs to Deborah Sampson. In May, 1782, she dressed in a shirt, pants, and boots, and enlisted in the Army under the name of Robert Shurtleff. Sampson fought in many battles and concealed her identity as a woman for a year until she was hospitalized for a high fever. General Washington gave her an honorable discharge from the Army. She was awarded a pension from the government for her military service.

Heroic Women in the Revolutionary War

RESEARCH QUESTIONS

1. In a dictionary, find the following words: *heroine, untraditional, assemble, retreat, pension, enlist, conceal, identity,* and *discharge.* Define each word and use it in a sentence.

2. Choose one of the heroines in your reading: *Sybil Ludington, Molly Pitcher, Margaret Corbin,* or *Deborah Sampson.* Find out about her life and accomplishments. Present your findings to the group as if you were inducting her into the American Hall of Fame.

3. Margaret Corbin is buried in the cemetery at *West Point.* What is West Point? Where is it located? Can anyone be buried there? Write your findings in a one-page summary.

PROJECTS

1. Read *Sybil Rides for Independence* by Drollene P. Brown. Illustrate the story by making it into a cartoon strip story.

2. Find pictures of Deborah Sampson. Draw her *portraits* before she joined the Army and later when she was known as Robert Shurtleff.

3. Draw the design for a statue of Molly Pitcher in action during the American Revolution.

4. Read *This Time, Tempe Wicks?* by Patricia Lee Gauch. Write what you would have done with the bothersome Revolutionary soldiers.

Sybil's Ride

Help Sybil Ludington and her horse, Star, find her way home after she warns the Minutemen that the British are on the march!

HOME!

Spies

In the 1770s, there were no telephones, televisions, radios, postal service, airplanes, cars, trains, or buses to communicate across long distances. During the Revolutionary War, information was gathered and passed along through a network of spies.

A spy could look like any other citizen. The whole point to being a spy is to deliver the information to the contact person without drawing attention to yourself.

Loyal patriots found clever ways to deliver a message. They developed a system of signals for watching contact persons, such as a specific color of flower in a flower pot, a certain pattern knitted into the stockings worn by the spy, a certain kind of buttons worn on a jacket, or a specific song sung in a public tavern. Spies were creative with finding hiding places for written messages as well. Messages could be found hidden in false heels and soles of boots, in coat linings, under wigs, in cut-out books, and within real letters.

The most famous American spy for the patriots during the Revolution was Nathan Hale. A schoolteacher from South Coventry, Connecticut, Hale volunteered to go behind British lines and obtain information. He passed through their lines disguised as a Dutch schoolteacher. He gathered the information, hid it in the lining of his shoe sole, and was returning to Connecticut when he was captured by the British. They found the information in his shoe, and hanged him for treason on September 22, 1776.

Another famous spy of the American Revolution was one who betrayed America—General Benedict Arnold. A career officer, Arnold worked with Ethan Allen and the Green Mountain Boys to capture Fort Ticonderoga in 1775 and won distinction in 1776 at the battle of Lake Champlain. However, he was angry that the Army promoted other men over him and he was in debt from living beyond his means. After he was made the commander of West Point, he agreed to hand it over to British General Clinton for $20,000 and a command in the British army. The plan was ruined when a spy was caught with details of the take-over. Arnold escaped to New York where he fought for the British, and then to England.

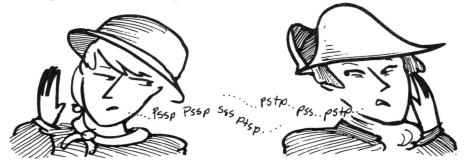

Spies

RESEARCH QUESTIONS

1. In a dictionary, find the following words: *sole, disguise, treason, promote,* and *debt*. Define each word and use it in a sentence.

2. Choose one of the spies in the reading, either *Nathan Hale* or *Benedict Arnold*. Research the details of his life. Write an *obituary* for him to be published in *Spy News*.

3. The spy who was caught passing information about Benedict Arnold was *Major John André*. Find out more about Major André. Why did the Americans admire him if he was a spy for the British? Make a "Spy Information Folder" about him, including a one-page summary of your findings and a drawing of him.

PROJECTS

1. Nathan Hale's home is preserved today in South Coventry, Connecticut. Draw a picture of what you think his home looks like.

2. If you were a spy during the American Revolution, where would you hide a message? Illustrate.

3. Recipe for invisible ink:
      4 drops of onion juice
      4 drops of lemon juice
      pinch of sugar
      shallow bowl
      toothpick
      paper
Stir together the onion juice, lemon juice, and sugar in the shallow bowl. Use the toothpick to write your message. As the "ink" dries your message will disappear. Hold the message over a bright bulb and your message will magically reappear!

Crack the Code

Resourceful spies during the American Revolution learned to send many different coded messages to their contact person. A good way to send a coded message was to send a code inside of a code. One of the easiest codes of this type was the First Letter Code.

To successfully decide a message using the First Letter Code, take the first letter of each word in the message to form the *real* message. For example, if the message says:

> Tarry here in silence; should he obey us, let's delay.
> Beware ever, else all shall yield.

then the *real* message, taking the first letters of each word, is:

THIS SHOULD BE EASY

Decode this message on the line below:

> Many earnest, eager teachers have even raged
> every time other new instructors get help, too.

_____

Write your own message on the lines below, and pass it along to a friend to see if they can crack YOUR code!

_____

_____

The Constitution and the Bill of Rights

Once the Revolution was over, the colonists had to decide how to organize and run the government they had fought so hard to win. In 1781, Congress passed the Articles of Confederation which laid down basic laws for the new country. However, the Articles declared each state independent of the others, in time leading to problems when states would not work together for the good of the nation. Each state issued its own money, and money that was good in one state was worth little in another. In 1786, Daniel Shays and other farmers revolted against the Massachusetts state government over unfair taxes and foreclosures on family farms. Clearly, the nation needed a strong central government to bring order and consistency to Americans' lives.

The Constitutional Convention was called in Philadelphia, Pennsylvania, on May 25, 1787. Twelve states sent delegates to the Convention. Rhode Island sent no one. George Washington was elected president of the convention. Other famous delegates to the convention were Benjamin Franklin, Alexander Hamilton, and "the father of the Constitution," James Madison.

The Constitution is divided into a preamble, or introduction, and seven articles, or sections. The preamble begins with the famous words, "We, the people of the United States..." The first section explains the legislative, or law-making, branch of the government. The second section details the executive, or presidential, branch of the government. The third section outlines the duties of the judicial, or interpreting the laws, branch of the government. The fourth section deals with relations between the states. The fifth section tells how the Constitution may be amended, or changed. The sixth section covers general information. The seventh section involves the ratification, or approval, of the Constitution by at least nine out of the twelve states represented (all twelve ratified the Constitution in time).

Patrick Henry would not sign the Constitution because he felt that it did not guarantee specific rights of the individual citizens. He helped write the first ten amendments to the Constitution, which have become known as the Bill of Rights. Today there are twenty-seven amendments to the Constitution.

The Constitution may be viewed today in the National Archives Building in Washington, D.C.

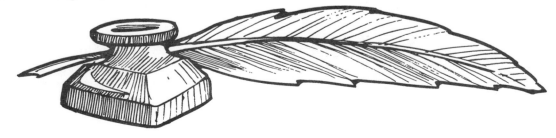

The Constitution and the Bill of Rights

RESEARCH QUESTIONS

1. In a dictionary, find the following words: *article* (not a part of speech), *confederation, revolt* (verb), *foreclosure, consistency, preamble, legislative, executive, judicial, ratify*, and *amendment*. Define each word and use it in a sentence.

2. Find out more about Daniel Shays and his rebellion. Present your information to the group as if you were a television news reporter.

3. Who was James Madison, and why is he known as "the father of the Constitution?" Write a one-page summary on James Madison, then write a one-page summary on his interesting wife, Dolley.

PROJECTS

1. George Washington trusted Alexander Hamilton, who signed the Constitution, more than any of his advisors. If Hamilton was that good, why didn't he ever become President? Read about Alexander Hamilton, then write his *obituary* for the *Washington Post*.

2. Shays' Rebellion was about discontented farmers on the western frontier. Read *Tree of Freedom*, by Rebecca Caudill, for a look at the Revolution from a backwoods settler's point of view.

3. Write your own Bill of Rights. Write down ten ideas that you believe are your basic rights as a kid.

4. Your class has just formed a new state. Design a one dollar bill for your class to represent your new state.

American Symbols from the Revolutionary War

When someone says, "America," what comes to your mind? Do you think of the American flag, the Liberty Bell, or maybe the bald eagle? These are all symbols of America, and they were created at the time of the Revolutionary War.

When the colonists were going into battle, they wanted to have a banner or flag to carry before them as a symbol of the nation for whom they were fighting. The legend of the beginning of the American flag tells of General George Washington ordering the flag from seamstress Betsy Ross. There is no proof that this actually happened, but General Washington's family coat-of-arms included red and white bars and five-pointed stars. The red stripes stand for the blood shed by brave colonists in the battle for their independence from Britain. The white stripes symbolize purity, truth, and liberty. There are thirteen stripes on the flag, one for each of the original thirteen colonies. The stars on a field of dark blue represent the stars in the heavens, and there is one star for each state in the Union, or fifty stars in all.

The Liberty Bell hangs today in Independence Hall in Philadelphia, Pennsylvania. It was cast in England in 1752, and it was created to celebrate Philadelphia's Golden Jubilee. When the bell was rung the first time, it cracked. Even though it was recast twice, the bell continued to crack. The bell was rung again on July 8, 1776, in honor of the signing of the Declaration of Independence. During the Revolutionary War, the bell was removed and hidden in the town of Allentown. It has not been rung since the anniversary of George Washington's birthday in 1846.

The national symbol for America is the bald eagle, shown on the Great Seal of the United States. When the founding fathers of America were deciding on an animal to represent the new nation, Benjamin Franklin wanted the turkey because it is native to America and is less threatening than an eagle. The independence and strength of the eagle won out, and it is seen holding in its claws arrows for war and an olive branch for peace. The design for the Great Seal was started in 1776 and completed in 1788.

The song "Yankee Doodle Dandy" originated during the Revolutionary War. At first it was sung by British soldiers to make fun of the shabby, ragged clothing worn by the colonial army. However, the tune became popular in the colonies and became the battle song for many troops heading into battle. "Yankee Doodle Dandy" was played as the "Mohawk Indians" marched away from the tea-stained Boston Harbor after the Boston Tea Party.

American Symbols from the Revolutionary War

RESEARCH QUESTIONS

1. In a dictionary, find the following words: *symbol, liberty, shed* (verb), *purity, founding, threatening, originate,* and *shabby.* Define each word and use it in a sentence.

2. The words on the Great Seal of the United States are: E PLURIBUS UNUM. What do the words mean, and from what language do they come?

3. What is the symbolism of lighting *fireworks* on the Fourth of July? Find out more about fireworks. In what country were they invented? How are fireworks made? What are some specific kinds of fireworks displays? Write a one-page summary on your findings and include illustrations.

PROJECTS

1. Read *Doodle Dandy!* by Lynda Graham-Barber. Choose your favorite symbol of America and create it out of found materials, such as tissue paper, paper tubes, glitter, sequins, crepe paper, popsicle sticks, paper stars, and construction paper.

2. Look carefully at the symbols on the back of our one dollar bill. What is the pyramid for? What is the eye for? And what could ANNUIT COEPTIS NOVUS ORDO SECLORUM mean?

3. The "Spirit of '76" is a famous symbol for the United States dating from the American Revolution. Find pictures of the famous flag bearer, fife player, and drummer. Find two friends, dress-up like the trio, and reenact this scene from American history.

A Gobbler on the Great Seal?

Benjamin Franklin has a problem. He wants to show the Continental Congress what the Great Seal of the United States would look like if the turkey were on the nation's symbol, not the bald eagle. He comes to you, the best artist in Philadelphia, to draw the design in the space below. Don't forget to use arrows and an olive branch in your illustration.

Timeline of the Revolutionary Period

March 5, 1770	British soldiers kill five colonists in the Boston Massacre.
December 16, 1773	"Mohawk Indians" dump tea into Boston Harbor in Boston Tea Party.
April 19, 1775	Minutemen and Redcoats clash at Lexington and Concord.
May 10, 1775	Benedict Arnold and Ethan Allen take over Fort Ticonderoga.
June 15, 1775	Congress names George Washington Commander-in-Chief of the Continental Army.
June 17, 1775	British drive Americans from Breed's Hill near Bunker Hill.
July 4, 1776	Declaration of Independence was adopted by the thirteen colonies.
September 22, 1776	Nathan Hale is the first American spy hung by the British during the Revolution.
September 26, 1776	The British occupy Philadelphia.
December 26, 1776	Washington mounts a surprise attack on the Hessian troops at Trenton.
October 17, 1777	Burgoyne surrenders at Saratoga.
December 19, 1777	Washington's army winters at Valley Forge.
February 6, 1778	Benjamin Franklin is instrumental in the signing of an alliance between America and France.
December 29, 1778	Redcoats take over Savannah.
September 23, 1779	John Paul Jones' *Bonhomme Richard* captures the British *Serapis*.
May 12, 1780	Charleston falls to the British.
September 5, 1781	French fleet blocks British naval force in Chesapeake Bay.
October 19, 1781	Cornwallis surrenders to Washington at Yorktown.
November 30, 1782	Treaty of Paris is signed.
June, 1783	Deborah Sampson hospitalized, then honorably discharged from Army.
May 25, 1787	Beginning of the Constitutional Convention in Philadelphia.